P9-ARM-009

YOUR SKIN AND MINE

THOMAS Y. CROWELL COMPANY
NEW YORK

YOUR

SKIN

AND

MINE

By Paul Showers
Illustrated by Paul Galdone

LET'S-READ-AND-FIND-OUT SCIENCE BOOKS

Editors: *DR. ROMA GANS*, Professor Emeritus of Childhood Education, Teachers College, Columbia University
DR. FRANKLYN M. BRANLEY, Chairman and Astronomer of The American Museum-Hayden Planetarium

*AVAILABLE IN SPANISH

ISBN: 0-690-91126-2
0-690-91127-0 (LB)

Published in Canada by Fitzhenry & Whiteside Limited, Toronto

YOUR SKIN AND MINE

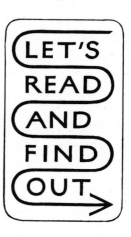

Henry's skin is light brown.
Mark's skin is dark brown.

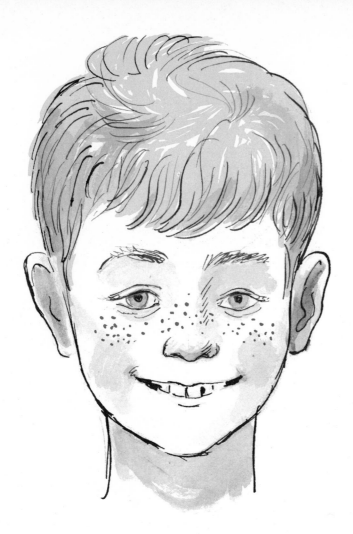

My skin is white with freckles.
If I stay out in the sun too long, my skin turns red—
And I get more freckles.

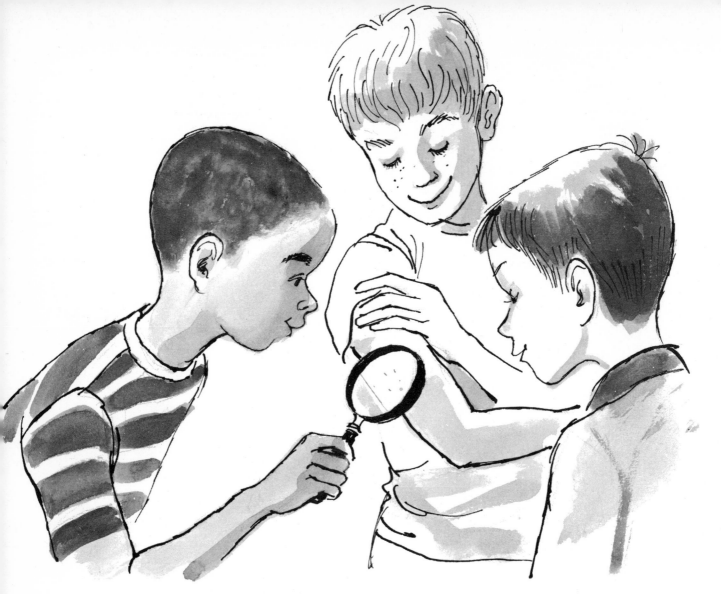

Sometimes Henry and Mark and I look at our skin
    under a magnifying glass.
You can do the same thing.

With a magnifying glass you can see the hair that
  grows out of your skin.
Short hairs grow on your arms and legs, and long
  hairs grow on your head.

Each hair grows out of a little hole called a follicle.
A follicle is a kind of tiny pocket.
The hair grows up from the bottom of the follicle.
It sticks out of the follicle the way a flower sticks
out of a vase.
A follicle has oil in it, too.
The oil keeps the hair soft and shiny.
It oozes out of the follicle and helps to keep the skin
from getting too dry.

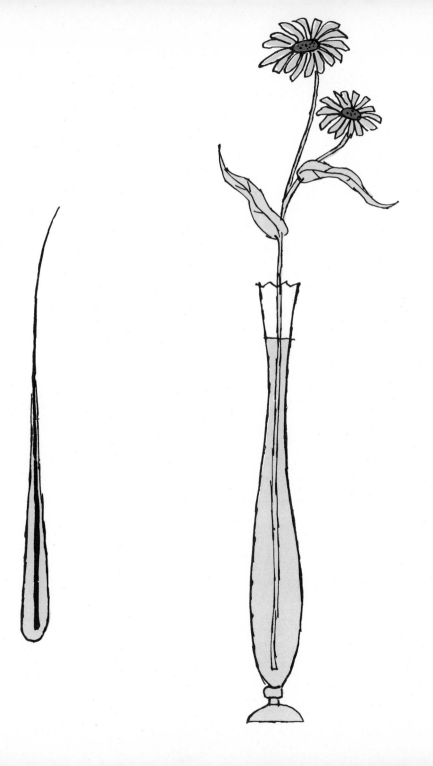

Fingernails and toenails are part of your skin.
They protect the tips of your fingers and toes.
They are like your hair because they keep growing
all the time.

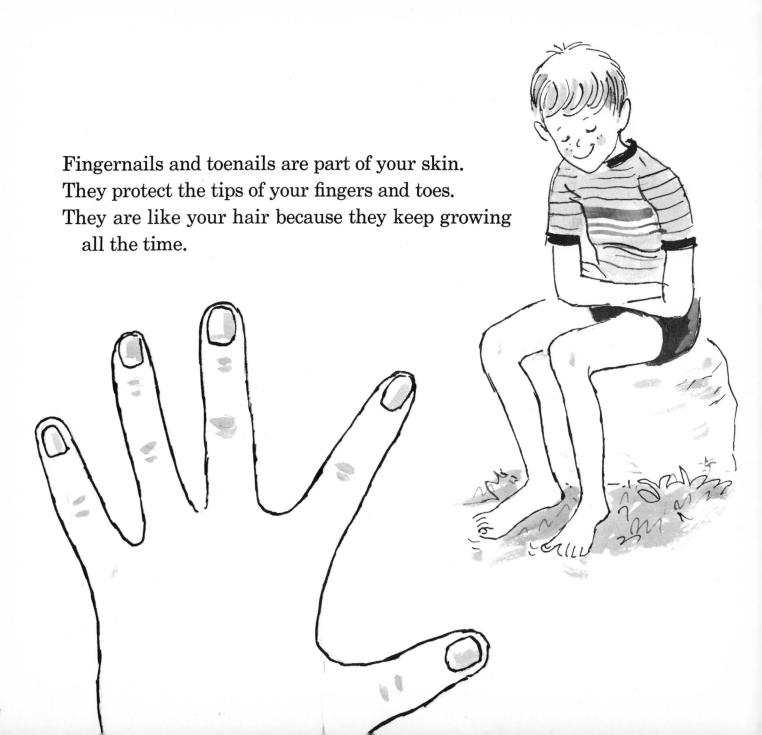

When you cut your hair you don't feel anything.
When you cut your nails you don't feel anything
    either.

The rest of your skin has feeling.
We made up a game about this.
One of us is blindfolded.
Then the others try to touch him so gently he can't
    feel anything.

We touch him VERY gently on

his cheek—

his wrist—

his ankle—

his ear.

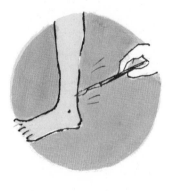

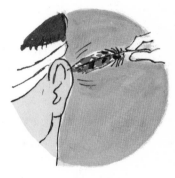

We touch him with
a piece of paper—

a balloon—

a paintbrush—

a feather.

It is hard to fool him. He can feel even a very light
touch on his skin.

Look at your fingertips under the magnifying glass.
You can see loops and lines.
They are ridges in your skin. They tell you whether
    something is rough or smooth.

You can make prints of the ridges on your fingertips.
Rub your fingers in some fingerpaint. Press the tips
  down on a piece of white paper.
Lift your hand carefully.
Your fingerprints show loops and lines.
You can see them better under the magnifying glass.

These are Mark's fingerprints
under the magnifying glass.

These are Henry's fingerprints
under the magnifying glass.

Everybody's fingerprints are different.

Footprints are different, too.

In hospitals nurses make footprints of new babies.
You can always tell one baby from another by his
footprint.

Your skin helps you to keep warm and to keep cool.
When you are cold, you shiver.
Your skin makes "goosebumps."
It does that to help make you warmer.

When you play in the sun on a hot day, you become
   sweaty.
Sweat is water that comes from inside your body.
Your skin lets it out through tiny holes called pores.
As the sweat dries up, your skin becomes cooler.

Most of the pores in your skin are smaller than hair
  follicles.
You cannot see the pores, even with the magnifying
  glass.
But you can see the drops of sweat that come out of
  them.

Skin covers your body from the top of your head to
   the soles of your feet.
Skin helps keep dirt and germs out of your body.

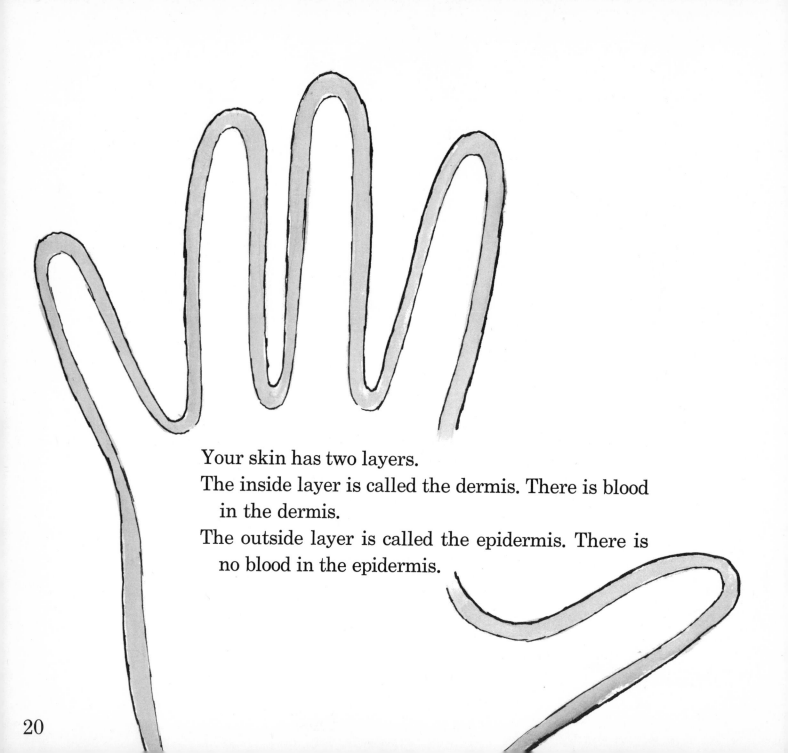

Your skin has two layers.
The inside layer is called the dermis. There is blood
    in the dermis.
The outside layer is called the epidermis. There is
    no blood in the epidermis.

20

The epidermis keeps rubbing off a little bit at a time.
When you rub yourself hard with a towel, you often
   rub off a bit of your epidermis.
It comes off in little pieces, all rolled up.

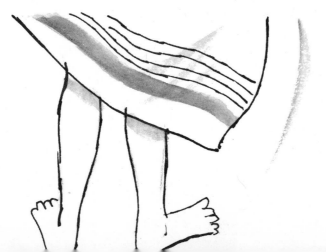

Sometimes you rub off more epidermis than you
    want to.
The other day we were climbing trees. I slid down
    too fast and skinned my leg.
I had scraped off a piece of epidermis.
Part of it was wrinkled up at one side of the scraped
    place.

I could see the dermis layer of my skin. It was pink.
It stung and smarted but it didn't bleed.
A clear, sticky fluid oozed out of the dermis until it
   covered all the scraped part.
That made the dermis stop smarting, and we went
   on playing.
The sticky fluid dried and made a crust, which is
   called a "scab."
My father says a "scab" is something like a bandage.
It keeps out germs until new epidermis can grow.
Then the "scab" falls off.

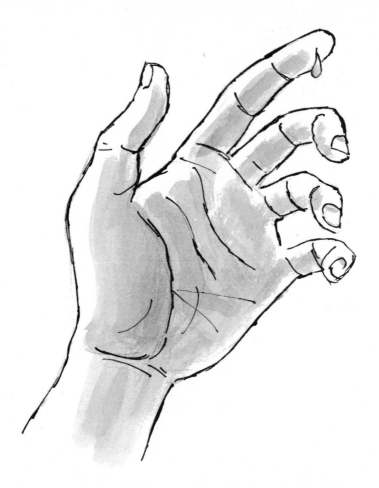

Yesterday Mark cut his finger with his knife.
He cut through the epidermis and into the dermis.
Red blood came out of the cut.

His father washed Mark's hand with soap and water.
Then he put a bandage over the cut.
That was to help stop the bleeding and to keep out
   germs.
The bandage was like a "scab."

25

Your skin protects you from the sun.
It does this by making grains of color called melanin.
Some melanin grains are brown. Others are tan.
  They are very tiny.
The skin makes millions of melanin grains.
They are in the skin and they give color to the skin.
Melanin makes a kind of screen that keeps out some
  of the burning sunlight.

Everybody's skin makes melanin.

Some skin makes a lot of melanin.

Other skin doesn't make very much.

Mark's skin makes a lot of black melanin.

Henry's skin does not make so much melanin as
Mark's and it is brown.

My skin makes light brown melanin. It doesn't make
very much.

Some of the melanin in my skin is gathered in spots.
These are my freckles.

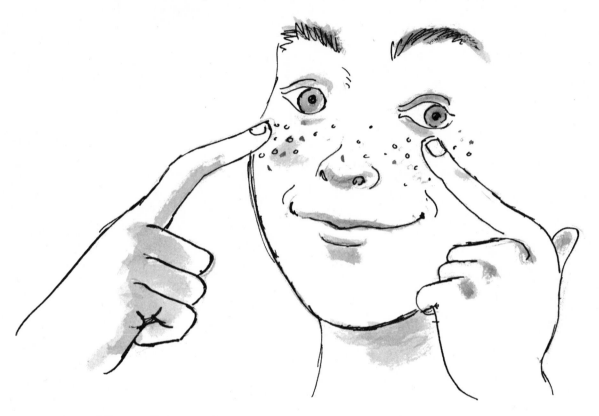

Your skin makes more melanin when the sun shines
 on it.
It makes more melanin in summer to protect your
 body from the burning sunlight.
That is what makes you tan.

Skin is easy to keep clean.

It is easier to clean than cloth or paper or almost
  anything.

Yesterday we were very dirty.

My sister and I helped Mother clean the attic.

Mother made us wear our bathing suits.

The attic was full of dust and cobwebs.

It was hot in the attic; we became sweaty and dirty.

31

When we were finished, we soaped ourselves and
    turned the hose on each other.
In two minutes we were clean.
Mother said that was easier than washing our dirty
    clothes.

She made us cold lemonade.
We sat under the trees. The breeze blew on our wet
    skin.

We were cool, inside and outside.

ABOUT THE AUTHOR

PAUL SHOWERS is a newspaperman and writer. Starting out as a copy editor on the *Detroit Free Press* and later the *New York Herald Tribune*, he spent the war years as a sergeant on the staff of *Yank*, the Army weekly. Subsequently he worked briefly for the *New York Sunday Mirror* and then joined the staff of *The New York Times*, where he is now assistant travel editor.

Mr. Showers was born in Sunnyside, Washington, and grew up in various parts of the country, among them a suburb of Chicago, Muskegon and Grand Rapids in Michigan, and Rochester, New York. He now lives in Brooklyn, New York.

ABOUT THE ILLUSTRATOR

PAUL GALDONE is one of this country's outstanding illustrators of children's books. He studied at the Art Students League of New York and with George Grosz, and he spent his spare time sketching from life in parks, zoos, subways, and streets, and doing New England summer landscapes on his vacations.

Mr. Galdone is a native of Budapest, Hungary, and lives now in Rockland County, New York.